# Gold Stars®

# Starting Phonics

## Pre-school

Written by Betty Root

PaRragon

Bath · New York · Singapore · Hong Kong · Cologne · Delhi · Melbourne

# Helping your child

⭐ Remember that the activities in this book should be enjoyed by your child. Try to find a quiet place to work.

⭐ Your child does not need to complete each page in one go. **Always stop before your child grows tired**, and come back to the same page another time.

⭐ It is important to work through the pages in the right order because the activities do get progressively more difficult.

⭐ Phonics help children to understand that letters and groups of letters make different sounds. Blending them together makes words. Learning about phonics helps children to read.

⭐ The answers to the activities are on page 32.

⭐ Always give your child lots of encouragement and praise.

⭐ Remember that the gold stars and badges are a reward for effort as well as for achievement.

Illustrated by Simon Abbott

This edition published by Parragon in 2010

Parragon
Queen Street House
4 Queen Street
BATH, BA1 1HE, UK

ISBN 978-1-4075-7527-8
Printed in China

# Contents

# Letter sounds a–m

Trace each letter. Draw a ring around two pictures in each row that begin with the same sound.

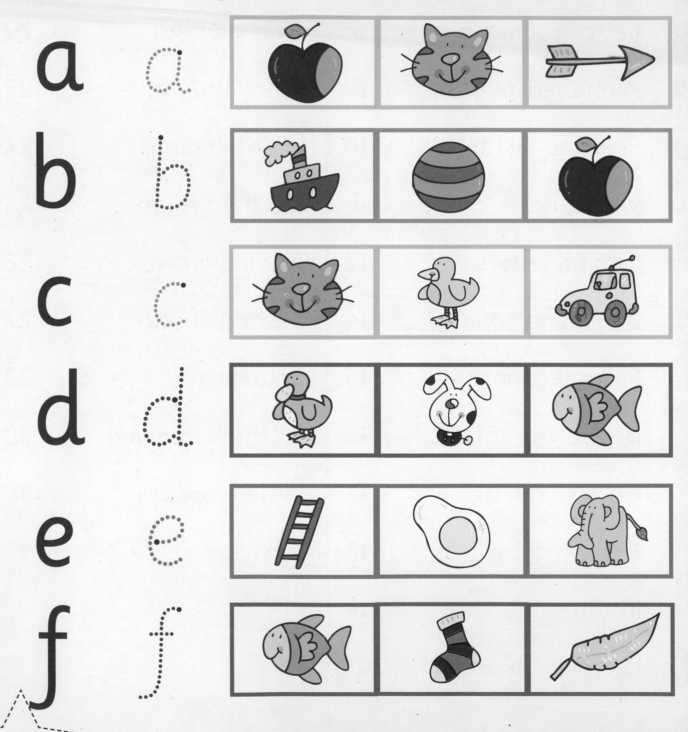

Note for parent: This activity helps children to understand beginning sounds and to write them.

g

h

i

j

k

l

m

Trace each letter. Draw a ring around two pictures in each row that begin with the same sound.

n n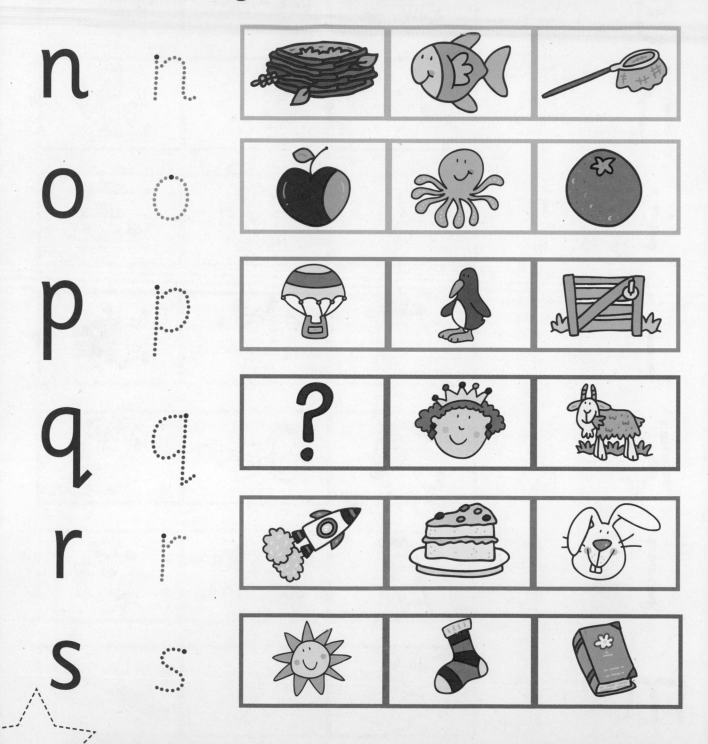

o o

p p

q q

r r

s s

t

u

v

w

x

y

z

t

u

v

w

x

y

z

# Alphabetical order

Join the letters of the alphabet to make these pictures.

## a b c d e f g

## h i j k l m n

Note for parent: This activity helps to teach alphabetical order.

# o p q r s t

# u v w x y z

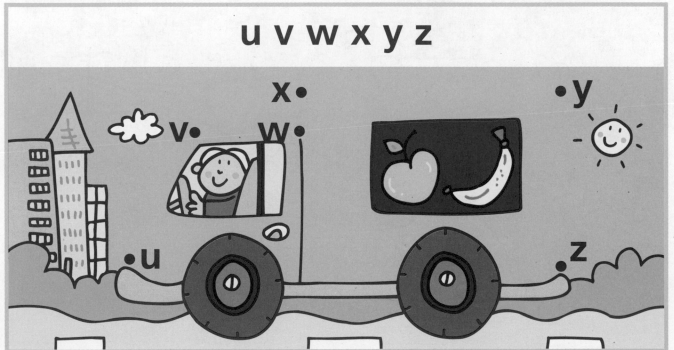

# Find the pictures

Say the sound of each letter. Look at the big picture and name something beginning with each sound.

**d  b  h  k**

**c  a  s  f**

Note for parent: This activity helps children to learn the beginning sounds a, b, c, d, f, h, k and s.

# Which letter?

Look at each picture. Choose the right letter and write it in the space to complete each word.

m     o

__ an

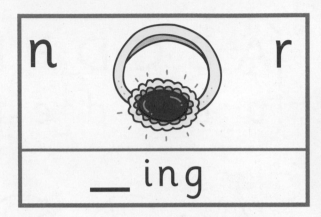

n     r

__ ing

s     p

__ ig

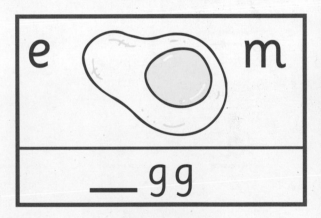

e     m

__ gg

g     p

__ ate

h     l

__ og

Note for parent: This activity helps children to learn the beginning sounds e, g, l, m, p and r.

# Capital letters

Trace each capital letter and write the matching small one beside it. The first one has been done for you.

| A | B | C | D | E | F | G | H | I | J | K | L | M |
|---|---|---|---|---|---|---|---|---|---|---|---|---|
| a | b | c | d | e | f | g | h | i | j | k | l | m |

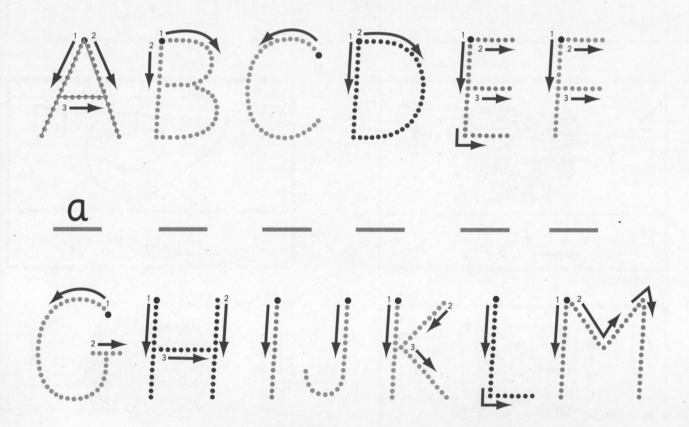

a _ _ _ _ _ _ _ _ _ _

_ _ _ _ _ _ _ _ _

# N O P Q R S T U V W X Y Z
## n o p q r s t u v w x y z

N O P Q R S T

U V W X Y Z

# Beginning sounds

Say the sound of each letter. Look at the big picture and name something beginning with each sound.

| | | | |
|---|---|---|---|
| **n** | **z** | **t** | **f** |
| **w** | **o** | **v** | **k** |

Note for parent: This activity helps children to learn the beginning sounds f, k, n, o, t, v, w and z.

# Second chance

Draw lines to join two pictures to each letter.

## a    b    c    d

Write the capital letters.

| a | f | h | w | p | b | e |
|---|---|---|---|---|---|---|
|   |   |   |   |   |   |   |

Note for parent: This page gives a chance to see what children can remember from earlier pages.

# Begins the same

Say the name of the picture in the middle of each box. Draw lines to join each middle picture to other pictures in the box that begin the same way.

Note for parent: This activity encourages children to speak clearly.

# Choose a letter

Choose the right letter from the boxes below to complete each word.

| f | h | t | b | k | z |
|---|---|---|---|---|---|

__ i s h

__ i r d

__ a t

__ i n g

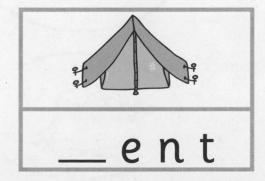

__ e n t

__ e b r a

# Find a rhyme

Draw lines to join the pictures that rhyme.

Note for parent: Recognizing rhyme helps children to listen carefully.

# In the same way

Say the name of the picture in the middle of each box. Draw lines to join each middle picture to other pictures that begin in the same way.

Note for parent: This activity encourages children to speak clearly.

# Learning **b** and **d**

Trace over the letters.

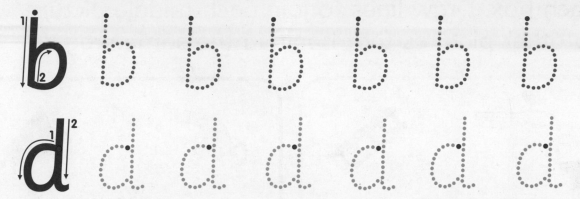

Choose the letter **b** or **d** to complete the words below.

_ice     _aby     _og     _oor

_all     _ook     _uck     _ed

# Sound the same

Draw lines to join the pictures that begin in the same way.

Note for parent: This activity encourages children to speak clearly.

# Odd one out

Cross out the odd picture inside each shape.

Note for parent: This activity helps children to recognize differences between beginning sounds.

# More than one

Write the missing word. Remember to add the letter **s** at the end because there is more than one object.

hat

\_ \_ \_ \_

sock

\_ \_ \_ \_ \_

bat

\_ \_ \_ \_

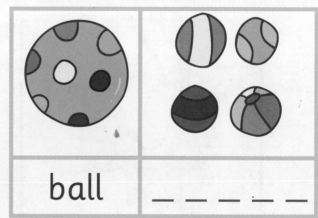

ball

\_ \_ \_ \_ \_

tree

\_ \_ \_ \_ \_

star

\_ \_ \_ \_ \_

# Word endings

Say the name of each picture. Draw a ring around the correct letter that comes at the end of each word.

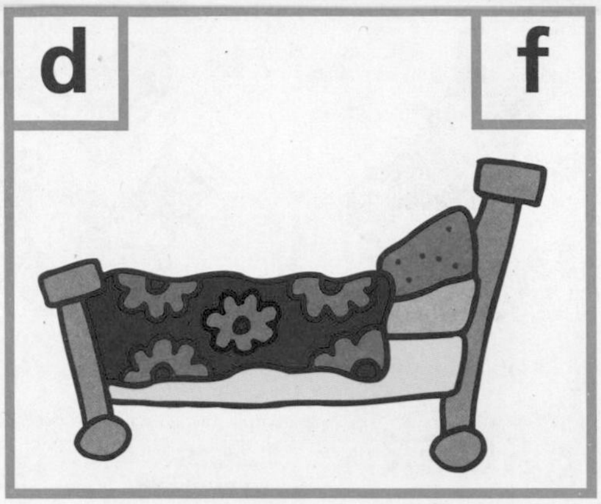


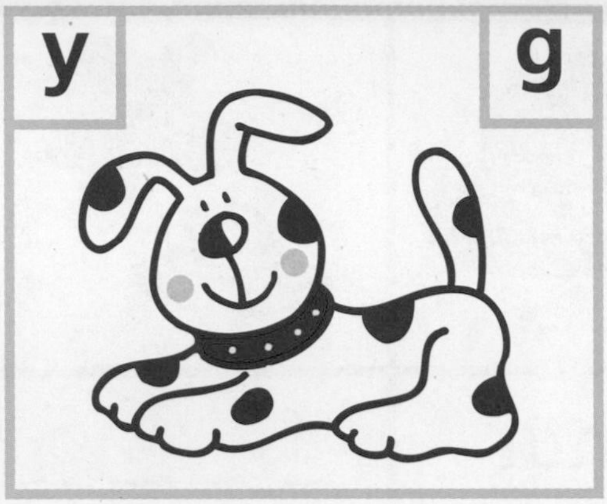


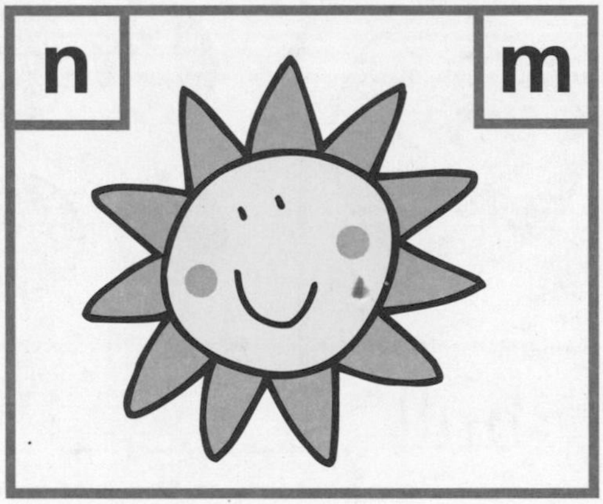

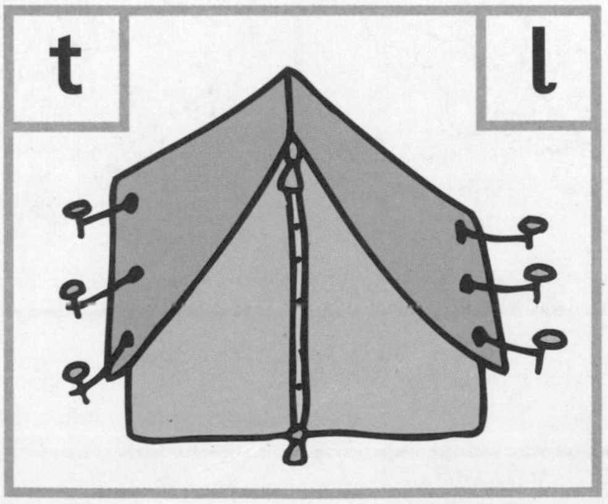


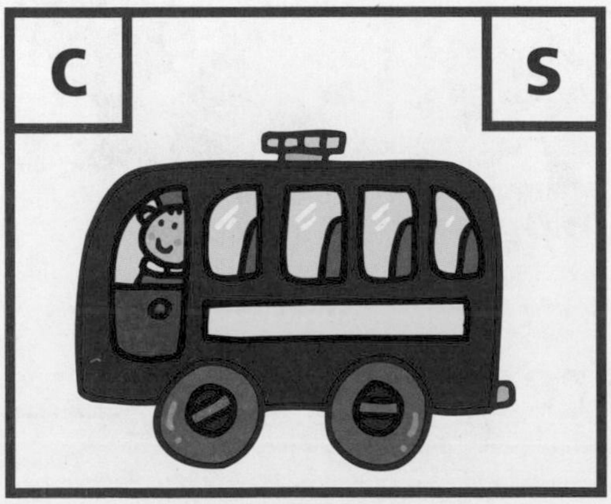




Note to parent: This activity encourages children to listen carefully to sounds at the end of words.

# Do they rhyme?

Do these pictures rhyme? Put a ✔ or a ✖ in the box under each pair of pictures.

★ Note for parent: Recognizing rhymes develops good listening skills.

# Finding words

Read the words under the pictures. Find the correct letters in the row of mixed-up letters and draw a ring around each one. Write the words in the spaces.

**owl**

a m b o j s r w c l

_ _ _

**moon**

b c m s r o t t o n

_ _ _ _

**cow**

a z c m s o g k w y

_ _ _

**drum**

e n d y r m r n u m

_ _ _ _

Note for parent: This activity helps children to recognize the letters that make an individual word.

# Second chance

Draw lines to join the pictures that rhyme.

Cross out the picture in each row that does not belong.

Draw a ring around the letter that comes at the end of each word.

d    f

y    g

 Note for parent: This page tests what children remember from earlier pages.

Trace over the letters. Say the sounds.

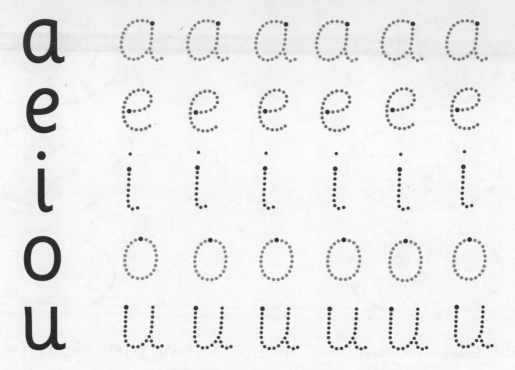

a  a a a a a a a

e  e e e e e e e

i  i i i i i i i

o  o o o o o o o

u  u u u u u u u

Name each picture. Tick the words with
an **a** sound in the middle.

Name each picture. Tick the words with
an **e** sound in the middle.

Note to parent: This activity helps children to identify the
vowels a, e, i, o and u.

Name each picture. Tick the words with
an **i** sound in the middle.

Name each picture. Tick the words with
an **o** sound in the middle.

Name each picture. Tick the words with
a **u** sound in the middle.

# At the beginning

Look at the pictures. Draw a ring around the correct beginning sound.

b d p

j y p

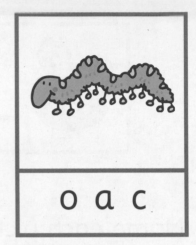

o a c

o a i

d b h

a o c

n u e

h l t

Note for parent: This activity helps children to recognize the letters a, c, d, h, j, o, t and u.

# Little words

Find the little words in the grid below.
Draw a ring around each word you find.

| | | | | |
|---|---|---|---|---|
| so | is | it | on | at |
| me | go | no | if | we |

| | | | | |
|---|---|---|---|---|
| i | s | b | a | t |
| w | e | m | e | p |
| g | h | i | t | v |
| s | o | r | g | o |
| w | q | o | n | x |
| n | o | p | i | f |

Note to parent: This activity encourages careful observation.

# Answers

## Pages 4–5

## Pages 6–7

## Page 10

Possible answers are: d – dog, b – ball, h – horse, k – kite, c – cake, a – apple, s – sandwich, f – fox.

## Page 11

<u>m</u>an <u>r</u>ing <u>p</u>ig e<u>gg</u> <u>gate</u> <u>log</u>

## Page 14

Possible answers are: n – nest, z – zebra, t – tiger, f – fox, w – window, o – owl, v – vase, k – kangaroo.

## Page 15

a = apple, astronaut; b = boat, ball; c = car, cat; d = duck, dog.
A F H W P B E

## Page 16

tree: <u>tr</u>iangle, <u>tr</u>ain, <u>tr</u>actor.
bridge: <u>br</u>ush, <u>br</u>ead, <u>br</u>icks.
flag: <u>fl</u>ipper, <u>fl</u>y, <u>fl</u>ower.

## Page 17

<u>f</u>ish, <u>b</u>ird, <u>h</u>at, <u>k</u>ing, <u>t</u>ent, <u>z</u>ebra.

## Page 18

hook/book, dog/frog, man/fan, moon/spoon, bee/tree.

## Page 19

spider: <u>sp</u>aghetti, <u>sp</u>oon, <u>sp</u>ade.
whale: <u>wh</u>eelbarrow, <u>wh</u>istle, <u>wh</u>eel.
sheep: <u>sh</u>oe, <u>sh</u>ark, <u>sh</u>ell.

## Page 20

dice, <u>b</u>aby, <u>dog</u>, <u>door</u>, <u>ball</u>, <u>book</u>, <u>duck</u>, <u>bed</u>.

## Page 21

clock/cloud/clown;
dress/dragon/drum;
green/grass/grapes.

## Page 22

## Page 23

hats, socks, bats, balls, trees, stars.

## Page 24

be<u>d</u>, do<u>g</u>, su<u>n</u>, boo<u>k</u>, ten<u>t</u>, bu<u>s</u>.

## Page 25

## Page 26

amb**o**jsr**wcl** – owl, bc**m**sr**ott**on – moon, az**c**ms**o**gk**w**y – cow, end**y**rmrn**um** – drum.

## Page 27

hook/book, dog/frog, man/fan.
book, ball.
bed, dog.

## Pages 28–29

## Page 30

## Page 31